Secrets
with Ciphers and Codes

by Joel Rothman and Ruthven Tremain

THE MACMILLAN COMPANY | Collier-Macmillan Ltd., London

The Macmillan Company
Collier-Macmillan Canada, Ltd., Toronto, Ontario

Library of Congress catalog card number: 69-18241

Printed in the United States of America

FIRST PRINTING

To
Les Wagman
and
Sarah Eustis

SECRETS with Ciphers and Codes

There are many ways to conceal a communication, from vanishing ink and foreign languages to secret codes and ciphers that only the sender and receiver know. Technically, a "code" replaces a word with a new word or symbol, while a "cipher" replaces each letter with a symbol. Generally though, and in this book, a code can be any system for disguising a message. The study of codes and ciphers is called cryptology.

The first code most people learn to use, and they learn it as children, is Pig Latin. It rearranges words and makes them sound ridiculous.

For words beginning with consonants, the consonants are moved to the end of the word and followed by AY.

SPEAK THIS CODE becomes EAKSPAY ISTHAY ODECAY

If a word begins with a vowel sound, WAY is added to the end of the word.

HONEST ABE becomes HONESTWAY ABEWAY

In another version, EGG is placed before every vowel sound.

I'VE GOT A SECRET becomes EGGIVE GEGGOT EGGA SEGGECREGGET

Either system is easy to learn. With practice, you can become fluent and speak it swiftly, to the confusion of untrained ears (and unwanted listeners).

ATSWHAY ATTHAY, AYPRAY ELLTAY?

EGGAN EGGEGG, YEGGOU EGGIDEGGIEGGOT!

Written messages can be changed slightly to give prying eyes (and unwanted lookers) a hard time.

One way is to change the spacings between the words. The letters of the message are written in order but the spaces are put in odd places:

IFYO UAR EREA DINGTH ISY OUH AVEAKE ENE YE

Another way is to eliminate the spaces. Running all the letters together makes it horrible to read:

THISMESSAGEISNONEOFYOURBUSINESSSOKEEPOUT

When there is time, a message can be written out and then each word scrambled. EXAMPLE could become MELAPEX. Here is a sentence to unscramble:

GRARSNEST LUDOW VAEH LOBRUTE SINDUNGRANTED HITS

This is truly a code because each word is replaced, but there's no set system to it.

On the following pages are a number of systems for encoding (putting into code) messages by substituting symbols (ciphers) for letters. Some codes have several variations and with most of them there will be a few practice words to encode and some ciphers to decipher. There is also a Secret Message with each code. You can check your progress by comparing your solutions with the decoded messages on the last page.

It's a good idea to have a supply of paper. No fair writing in the book. You might be wrong. For encoding practice, a pencil and two colors will be useful.

If you like to share secrets and enjoy solving puzzles, you are now ready to become a cryptologist.

Secret Code One: **LETTERS**

This is the simplest cipher of all. One letter stands for another letter. The code letter is the direct substitute for the one really meant. The listing of the alphabet with each letter's substitute is called the Key. The two easiest Keys have the code letters in alphabetical order. The first one substitutes the next letter in the alphabet for the letter intended.

PARTIAL KEY

REAL LETTER	A	B	C	D	E	F	G	H	I		X	Y	Z
CODE LETTER	B	C	D	E	F	G	H	I	J		Y	Z	A

PRINTED becomes QSJOUFE and NJYUVSF is really **MIXTURE**

The second easiest Key reverses the order:

REAL LETTER	A	B	C		H	I	J	K	L	M	N	O	P
CODE LETTER	Z	A	B		G	H	I	J	K	L	M	N	O

For practice, encode: **LEARNING** and decipher: SN CDBHOGDQ

Since a 26-letter alphabet can actually be arranged 17,534,411,353,330,679,808,000,000 different ways, it is important to know which arrangement, or Key, is being used. Here is a Key, arranged at random, for Secret Code One:

KEY

A	B	C	D	E	F	G	H	I	J	K	L	M
P	O	I	U	Y	T	R	E	W	Q	A	S	D

N	O	P	Q	R	S	T	U	V	W	X	Y	Z
F	G	H	J	K	L	Z	X	C	V	B	N	M

SECRET MESSAGE ONE

LGDY DPN ZEWFA ZEWL WL

P TGKYWRF SPFRXPRY

Secret Code Two: NUMBERS

Words in this code look very mysterious. The ciphers are now the numbers from 1 to 26. If the numbers are arranged in order, the Key looks like this:

KEY

A	B	C	D	E	F	G	H	I	J	K	L	M
1	2	3	4	5	6	7	8	9	10	11	12	13
N	O	P	Q	R	S	T	U	V	W	X	Y	Z
14	15	16	17	18	19	20	21	22	23	24	25	26

CAPTURE would become 3 1 16 20 21 18 5

5 19 3 1 16 5 4 would mean ESCAPED

For practice, encode these words: CATTLE THIEF

For practice, decode these ciphers: 6 15 18 1 18 5 23 1 18 4

Since 26 numbers can also be arranged in 17,534,411,353,330,679,808,000,000 different ways, it is important to know which arrangement is being used. Any one can be used, of course, as long as the sender and receiver know which it is. Here is the Key for Secret Code Two.

KEY

A	B	C	D	E	F	G	H	I	J	K	L	M
10	20	6	14	2	25	21	7	16	11	1	15	22
N	O	P	Q	R	S	T	U	V	W	X	Y	Z
12	3	24	9	17	26	23	4	19	13	5	18	8

SECRET MESSAGE TWO

23 7 16 26   15 3 3 1 26   15 16 1 2   10

15 3 12 21   25 3 3 23 20 10 15 15   26 16 21 12 10 15

Secret Code Three: TWO NUMBERS

The letters are placed in a box with five spaces across (rows) and five spaces down (columns). I and J can share a box since there is rarely confusjon about which of these two letters is meant. The Key identifies each letter by its row number, then its column number. For example, K is 25 and W is 52.

	COLUMN NUMBER				
	1	2	3	4	5
1	A	B	C	D	E
2	F	G	H	I/J	K
3	L	M	N	O	P
4	Q	R	S	T	U
5	V	W	X	Y	Z

(ROW NUMBER)

KEY

A	B	C	D	E	F	G	H	I	J	K	L	M
11	12	13	14	15	21	22	23	24	24	25	31	32

N	O	P	Q	R	S	T	U	V	W	X	Y	Z
33	34	35	41	42	43	44	45	51	52	53	54	55

For practice, decipher these numbers:

12 45 54   23 24 32   43 34 32 15   44 11 33 22 15 42 24 33 15 43

For practice, encode these words:

HE REQUESTS THAT FLAVOR

SECRET MESSAGE THREE

31 24 44 44 31 15   43 15 13 42 15 44 43   33 15 51 15 42

43 11 21 15   24 33   12 24 22   32 34 45 44 23

35 11 43 43
44 34
32 15

34 25

P.S. You can mystify all but your most confidential friends by placing the letters in the boxes in a different order.

I	V	X	N	J
A	R	C	S	Y
L	B	M	D	T
O	F	W	H	Z
E	P/Q	G	U	K

Secret Code Four: TIC TAC TOE

ONE CHART CODE

This code is set up by placing letters in the nine spaces of the familiar TIC TAC TOE diagram. The Key will be a combination of lines to show the proper space and a dot to show which letter in that space.

A B C	D E F	G H I
J K L	M N O	P Q R
S T U	V W X	Y Z

KEY

A	B	C	D	E	F	G	H	I	J	K	L	M

N	O	P	Q	R	S	T	U	V	W	X	Y	Z

For practice, encode these words:

THE HARVEST MOON LOOKS

For practice, decipher these symbols:

SECRET MESSAGE FOUR

10

TWO CHART CODE

A B	C D	E F
G H	I J	K L
M N	O P	Q R

S	T	U
V	W	X
Y	Z	

Now the Key will be combinations
of lines, dots and colors.
For practice, decipher this:

Encode these words: **BUT TIME FLIES**

THREE CHART CODE

A	B	C
D	E	F
G	H	I

J	K	L
M	N	O
P	Q	R

S	T	U
V	W	X
Y	Z	

The dots are no longer
needed. Now the Key
will just have lines
and colors.

Decipher this: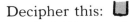

Encode this: **THE BLACK MONKEY WAVED RIGHT AT ME**

Secret Code Five: CRISS CROSS

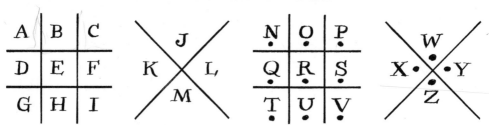

This is the old pigpen code that was used over 100 years ago during the Civil War. It is still called the Freemasons' cipher.

The four figures make 26 spaces, one for each letter of the alphabet. Dots in 13 of the spaces make it possible to draw a different symbol for each letter.

KEY

Decipher this:

Encode this:

THE FLAG IS FLYING

SECRET MESSAGE FIVE

Secret Code Six: SQUARES

The Keys for these codes will be colored squares and dots.

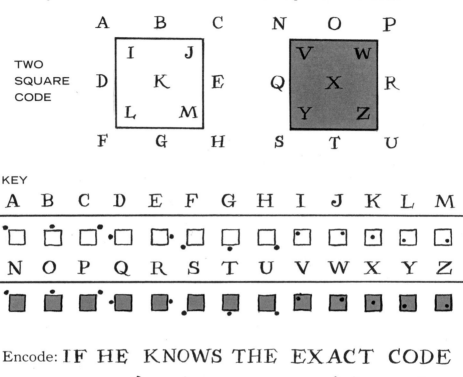

Encode: IF HE KNOWS THE EXACT CODE

Decipher: [symbols]

With more squares, all the dots move inside.

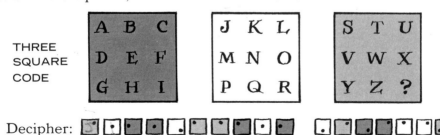

Decipher: [symbols]

Encode: IT IS JUST A NEW BOX

Secret Code Six: SQUARES continued

You can arrange the alphabet in as many squares as you like,
depending on how many colors and how much patience you have.

FOUR SQUARE CODE

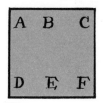 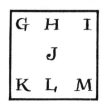 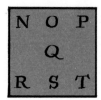 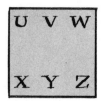

Encode: **JUST FED BACON TONIGHT**

Decipher: ◨ ◰ ◧ · ◰ ◧ · ◨ ◰ ◧ ◰ ◨ · ◧ ◧ ◨ ◰ ◧ · ◨

FIVE SQUARE CODE

With five spaces in five boxes for 25 letters, let I and J share a
space and hope you don't have to decipher IJGGLE.

SECRET MESSAGE SIX

14

When you run out of colors, you can use stripes.

SIX SQUARE CODE

Encode: **WHEN HE SAW THE FOX JUMP**

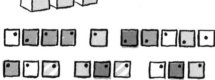

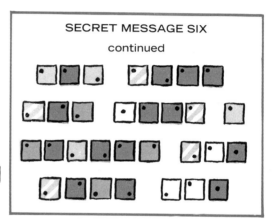

SECRET MESSAGE SIX
continued

SEVEN SQUARE CODE

Encode:

**LIKE TO
PUNCTUATE?
NOW YOU
CAN!**

Decipher:

Secret Code Six-A: SQUARES & DIAGONALS

The Keys will be combinations of triangles and dots.

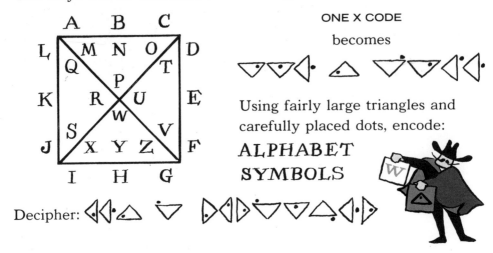

ONE X CODE

becomes

Using fairly large triangles and carefully placed dots, encode:

ALPHABET SYMBOLS

Decipher:

Again, with more squares, the dots all move inside.

TWO X CODE

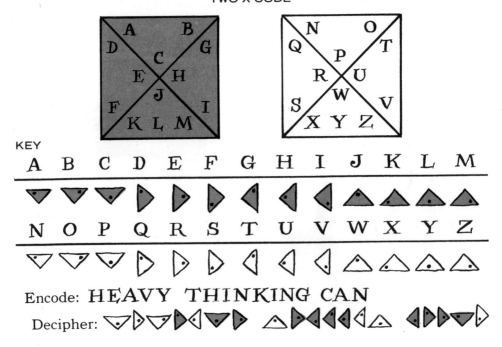

KEY

A	B	C	D	E	F	G	H	I	J	K	L	M

N	O	P	Q	R	S	T	U	V	W	X	Y	Z

Encode: **HEAVY THINKING CAN**

Decipher:

THREE X CODE

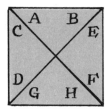  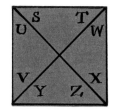

SECRET MESSAGE SIX-A

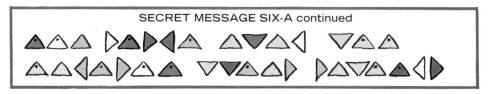

FIVE X CODE

Now dots are needed only for: D, I, L, O, T, Y.

SECRET MESSAGE SIX-A continued

No dots now.

SEVEN X CODE

Encode: ALONG WITH GAY STRIPES

Decipher:

17

Secret Code Six-B: SQUARES & SQUARES

ONE DOUBLE-SQUARE CODE

With nine letters in the center square,
the dots should be carefully placed.

Decipher:

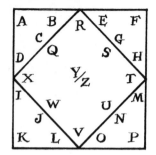

Encode: **VERY CONFUSING**

TWO DOUBLE-SQUARES CODE

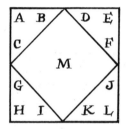

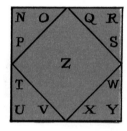

Decipher:

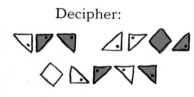

THREE DOUBLE-SQUARES CODE

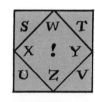

KEY

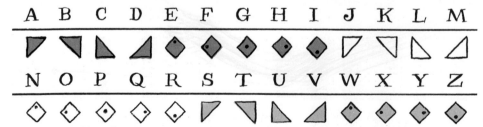

Encode: **LUCKY NEWS** Decipher:

ONE TRIPLE-SQUARE CODE

In the Key, the triangles can all
be about the same size.

Decipher:

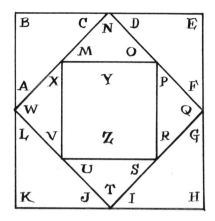

Encode: CRAZY QUILT

TWO TRIPLE-SQUARES CODE

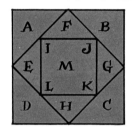 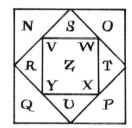

SECRET MESSAGE SIX-B

THREE TRIPLE-SQUARES CODE

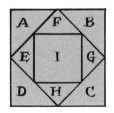 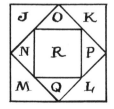 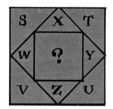

Decipher: ◥ ▽ ☐ ◁ ◥ ◥ ▽ ◁ ▽ ◿ ☐ ▽ ◀ ▷ ▷ ▽ ▷ ◣ ▣

Secret Code Seven: TRIANGLES

TWO SET CODE

A Set is a pair of triangles of the same color.

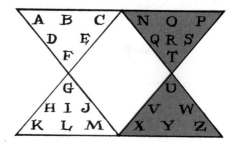

Decipher:

Encode: LEFT HAND

THREE SET CODE

FOUR SET CODE

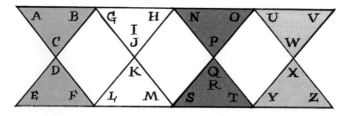

KEY

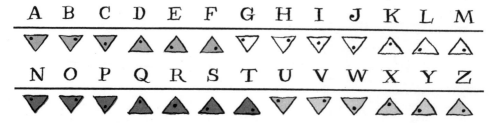

Encode: WHEN ELEPHANTS TRAVEL

FIVE SET CODE

Decipher:

SIX SET CODE

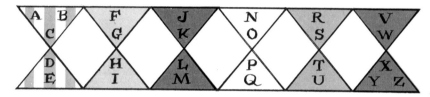

Encode: HEX SIGNS ON BARNS

Decipher:

SEVEN SET CODE

Encode: DIFFICULT?   Decipher:

SECRET MESSAGE SEVEN

Secret Code Seven: **TRIANGLES** continued

THREE BOW-TIES CODE

This is simply the Three Set Code standing on end.

Decipher: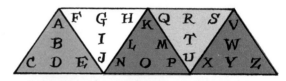

Encode: **WHAT BOAT NEVER GOES TO SEA?**

ZIGZAG CODE

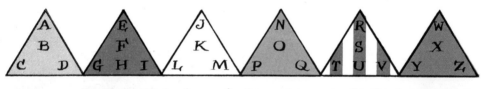

Decipher: △ ▽ ▽ △ △ △ △ △ ▽

SAWTOOTH CODE

Decipher: △△△△△ △ △△ △ △△△△△△

PYRAMID CODE

Here is a compact and pretty arrangement.

Encode: *OF RED AND BLUE*

Decipher:

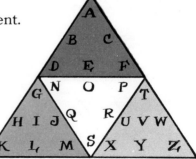

Secret Code Seven-A: & DIAMONDS

These are like the Sets with the diamond spaces between also used.

ONE DIAMOND CODE

Encode: THE TOOTHBRUSH IS

Decipher:

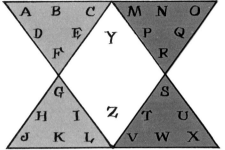

TWO DIAMOND CODE

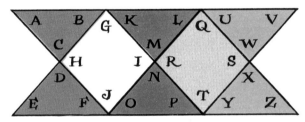

Encode: BUY SIX QUARTS OF MILK TONIGHT

SECRET MESSAGE SEVEN-A

Secret Code Eight: CIRCLES

TWO CIRCLE CODE

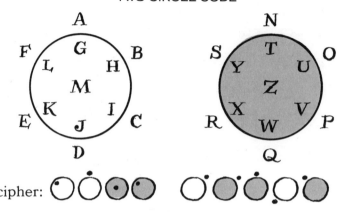

Decipher: ○ ○ ◖● ● ● ○̇ ○ ○̣ ○ ○

With more colors, you can have smaller circles and it's easier to spot the letters.

THREE CIRCLE CODE

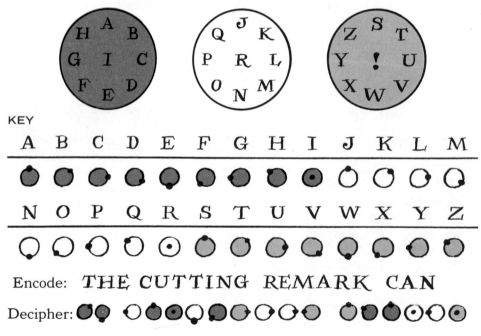

KEY

A	B	C	D	E	F	G	H	I	J	K	L	M

N	O	P	Q	R	S	T	U	V	W	X	Y	Z

Encode: THE CUTTING REMARK CAN

Decipher: ●● ○●●○●●○○○ ○●●●○○●

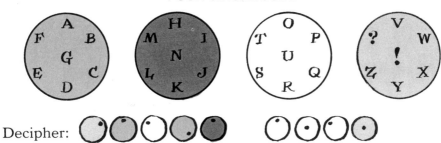

Decipher: ⬤⬤◯⬤⬤ ◯◯◯◯

Encode: THE PLAN IS TRICKY

SECRET MESSAGE EIGHT

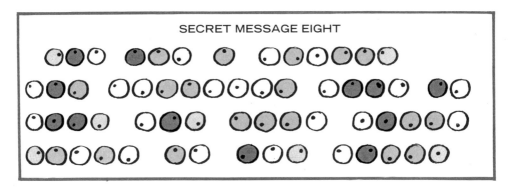

FIVE CIRCLE CODE

Decipher: ⬤⬤⬤⬤

⬤⬤⬤ ⬤⬤⬤

⬤⬤ ⬤⬤⬤⬤

Encode: YOU CAN'T
SEE VERY FAR

Secret Code Eight-A: HALF CIRCLES

The half circle is easy to draw and six
spots on its edge plus one in the middle
can be shown very accurately.

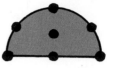

TWO SPLITS CODE

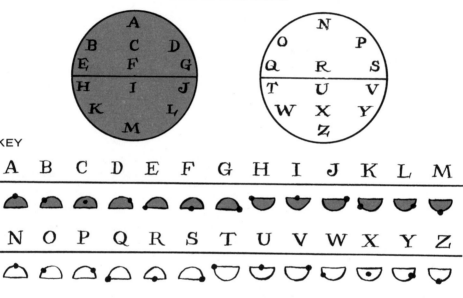

KEY

A	B	C	D	E	F	G	H	I	J	K	L	M

N	O	P	Q	R	S	T	U	V	W	X	Y	Z

Encode: THE WORLD IS NOT EXACTLY ROUND

THREE SPLITS CODE

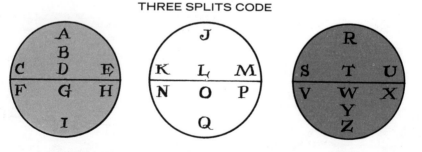

Decipher:

Encode: WHEN THE BELL RINGS

FOUR SPLITS CODE

Encode: Decipher:

THE WAY OUT

SECRET MESSAGE EIGHT-A

For variety, you can cut the circles up and down.

FIVE SPLITS CODE

Encode: Decipher:

ZIP ALONG WITH

The circles can also be cut on a slant.

SIX SLASHES CODE

Decipher:

27

Secret Code Eight-B: QUARTER CIRCLES

Little pie shapes and dots will form the Keys.

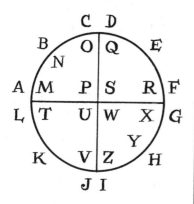

ONE Q CODE

Each quarter will have seven places for a dot, three around the outside, four inside.

Encode: **TRUE FACT**

SECRET MESSAGE EIGHT-B

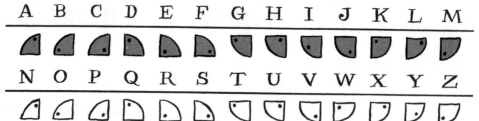

(secret message symbols)

Now all the dots move inside.

TWO Q CODE

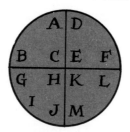

KEY

A B C D E F G H I J K L M

(symbol row)

N O P Q R S T U V W X Y Z

(symbol row)

Encode: **UNLUCKY PIRATES**

Decipher: *(symbols)*

28

THREE Q CODE

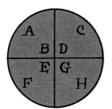  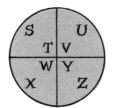

Encode: TO DAVY JONES LOCKER

Decipher:

FOUR Q CODE

SECRET MESSAGE EIGHT-B continued

Encode: WHICH PROVES

Decipher:

The circles can also be quartered on a slant.

SIX QX CODE

Dots are needed only for J and Q.

Decipher:

Secret Code Nine: COMBOS

Figures from the earlier codes can be combined in many other ways.

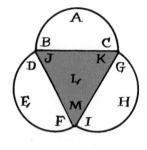

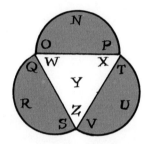

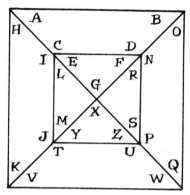

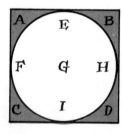

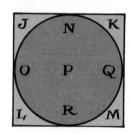

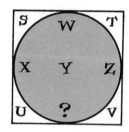

SECRET MESSAGE NINE

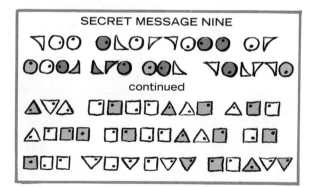

continued

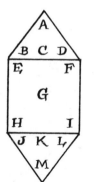

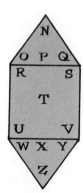

Secret Code Ten: **FANCIES**

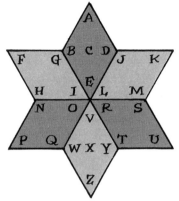

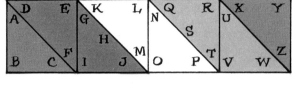

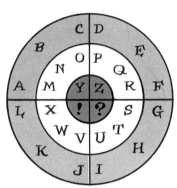

FINAL FANCY SECRET MESSAGE TEN

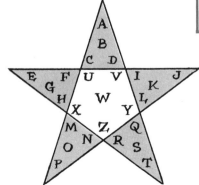

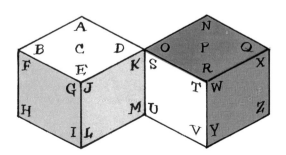

SECRET MESSAGES

ONE: SOME MAY THINK THIS IS A FOREIGN LANGUAGE

TWO: THIS LOOKS LIKE A LONG FOOTBALL SIGNAL

THREE: LITTLE SECRETS NEVER SAFE IN BIG MOUTH

FOUR: ONE EX-SPY HID SOME MICROFILM IN A PUMPKIN

FIVE: A PATRIOT IS A MAN WHO LOVES HIS COUNTRY

SIX: YOU CANNOT TIPTOE QUIETLY WHEN YOUR SPURS JINGLE
          (continued) AND WHEN YOU KNOW A SECRET ZIP YOUR LIP

SIX-A: MARK CONFIDENTIAL PAPERS FOR YOUR EYES ONLY
          (continued) YOU MIGHT EVEN ADD DESTROY AFTER READING

SIX-B: AN EXTRA SQUARE IS BETTER THAN A DOUBLE CROSS

SEVEN: A NEEDLE CAN BE FOUND IN A HAYSTACK WITH LUCK
          AND A MAGNET

SEVEN-A: A FAKE MESSAGE ON THE SAME PAPER MAKES THE
          REAL ONE LOOK LIKE SILLY DOODLING

EIGHT: WHO HAS A SCUBA? THE TREASURE SHIP IS ONLY
          SIX FEET UNDER WATER AT LOW TIDE !

EIGHT-A: OUR ALPHABET IS A BUNCH OF CODES BECAUSE
          THE LETTERS BEGAN AS SYMBOLS

EIGHT-B: EVERYONE GIVES AND NOBODY TAKES ADVICE
          (continued) PEOPLE WHO ASK FOR SOME DON'T
          REALLY WANT ANY

NINE: THE QUESTION IS WHOM CAN YOU TRUST?
          (continued) OLD FRIENDS ARE BEST FRIENDS
          IS THE LIKELY REPLY

TEN: KNOW WHAT? WITHOUT KEYS CIPHER EXPERTS
          CAN RECOGNIZE QUITE EASILY WHICH CODES ON THIS PAGE
          THESE SYMBOLS COME FROM AND DECIPHER THEM!